VOL 1
BECOMING HYPER-PRODUCTIVE

THE SIMPLE PATH
TO GETTING
EVERYTHING DONE

AND STILL HAVE ENERGY LEFT
TO SPARE

PATRICK LEROUGE

ISBN:

CONTENTS

Preface

I know what it feels like not to be the best version of yourself, not to live up to your potential, to fall short of your goals and not get what you think you want and need, to accept existing through life, like a small infant unaware of what it can be.

I remember I once lived in fear of making someone mad. I never stood tall. I became a jokester to keep the mood from going too low. I got good at avoiding anything that made me feel not good enough. This dimmed the light of who I am, and I no longer felt good being myself. My body began to deteriorate.

I had no clue that the writing was on the walls. I began to fear my pain, avoiding things I loved, playing small because I feared the pain. I would go as far as to project horrible things for the future, and I wouldn't even move off the couch because I had no energy. My focus on the pain drained all my motivation to do anything, yet I spent my nights tossing and turning, looking at the clock wondering when I would go to sleep. I constantly hoped and wished the next day would be different.

The writing was there the whole time, though, attempting to bring my attention to the fact I was not tapping into any of what I was capable of. We all have more within us. We just have to see the signals the mind and body are giving. That is the secret to reaching our highest potential.

I invite you to believe that you can shine and reach a level within yourself you did not know existed. That light you shine so brightly will attract likeminded people to you, people that will be your tribe, people that you will enjoy being around. You will be able to create a business that brings you wealth, that allows you to spend more time with your family instead of taking you away from it.

You will start feeling confident and powerful in your skin, feeling love for yourself with your clothes on and off. You will be more deliberate inside your body, with no aches and pains fighting for your attention. And you will intentionally create deep intimate relationships with your family and loved ones. You deserve all of these things.

As a massage therapist, in the year 2000, I dislocated my carpals (the small bones in the wrist), and the dean told me I was not going to be a good therapist. Massage therapists need their hands, and it was hard work. As much as I wanted to prove the dean wrong, she was right. I would do a massage and be in pain for days. I would learn a new trick/hack or brace my wrist to get relief. I was beginning to think I was permanently damaged. And the cycle never ended—do a massage, be in pain, not work for days, feel a little better, and then start all over again.

It went on like this for the first seven years of my massage career. I learned how to manage the pain and eventually ignored it altogether. But I sucked at massage because my pain always held me back.

Why did I keep doing it, then? I had in my head that I needed to man up to provide for myself and my wife. But because I compensated for my weak wrists, I began injuring other areas of my body, from my elbow to my shoulder to my neck. It was miserable; every treatment was torture.

I ended up attempting every modality technique for muscular pain and spent hours on self-care, ending with wearing braces at night, then meds. I went from doctor to physical therapy to chiropractors and alternative medicine providers. Nothing worked for me. After seven years of this, as a last-ditch effort, I went to an energy workshop that had high claims of healing the body doing less.

In my head, this was a perfect option because I was halfway down the path of not being able to work anyway.

Here is where the impossible became possible, I had my first healing experience with my eyes.

Since childhood, I had poor vision. It was so bad I had Coke-bottle lenses, which I was teased relentlessly for. Do you remember those big plastic frames with the heavy lenses? Man, it was bad. I was almost legally blind.

But the first day of the energy seminar was all it took—my life changed forever. It started out simply enough, with the seminar speaker asking some questions about what we wanted, as every seminar starts. I gave the traditional seminar answers:

- More money

- Less pain

Then he asked what about something you would never think was possible. What would that be?

I begrudgingly said my eye, but it was really just a throwaway statement to get him off my back. I didn't think I could be healed that way.

The next morning after the seminar, I was in my hotel in Las Vegas, on the top floor of the El Cortez Hotel. It is in the old section of Vegas, looking toward the new section. I woke up and walked to the window to look out, and I was able to see the Stratosphere Hotel and the mountains.

They were a little blurry, and I thought my glasses were dirty. But when I reached to take off my glasses, my jaw dropped to the floor. My glasses were across the room on the dresser next to the bed, which I also could see.

That morning, I was able to see. That morning, I learned my body was able to do what I never believed was possible: that my body can heal things that I never imagined.

I went back into the seminar and had a long talk with the energy practitioner about what he had done to me. He said something that baffled me for over ten years: "You can heal anything in an instant once you learn to decide." You decided yesterday to heal your eyes, so that's what happened.

To be completely honest I had no clue I had even done anything. I had only even said I wanted to fix my eyes to appease the practitioner and give him something I thought would be impossible to do

By the end of this book, you will see why out of all the things I asked for, the eye healing happened instantly.

This seminar was the beginning of a journey that has changed my life, and hopefully yours after you read this book. It taught me how to produce at a higher level—a level I had no clue I could reach.

By the end of the seminar, I left more confused and with way more questions then I went in with.

I could not understand how a pain that I accepted, a pain I had suffered with for so long, could go away so rapidly. Even though I lived it, I could not believe it.

How did this gift happen?

I did not have to work hard or even try to get it.

Can anyone do this, and why isn't it happening to everyone?

Sadly, because of those questions, within the year, my poor vision returned.

This set the events of the next several years in motion. I dedicated this time to getting my vision back. I needed to be able to do it on my own, not based on luck or circumstance.

I had to learn how to stay connected to my body, and I made it a priority to make time to connect, as well as become more productive while holding a connection. I started relying on natural energy to sustain healing.

I learned life happened for me, not to me.

I stopped worrying about the negative thoughts that kept me anxious and lowered my energy.

I learned grounding is not a sign of weakness. Being soft and caring took me further than being hard and ridged. Being grounded was a sign of strength. Becoming calm and slowing down during the fast, hard times were key, especially when I focused these learnings on improving my business.

When I stopped reacting to the world, I began to get ahead of it. I had to build a routine around the fact that I knew what I wanted and to get what I wanted.

I experienced a great feeling of accomplishment doing the routines I needed to do but never had the energy or consistency to do before. Once they became daily habits, I gained so much strength, and I found I could challenge myself daily.

I began being comfortable with coming up against my internal walls, and I practiced feeling safe while doing things that were uncomfortable. This was such a game-changer for my business and life. It allowed me to practice overcoming my blocks, time and time again. I faced my fears, which gave me the ability to live with confidence and honesty.

I built faith within myself, and I knew everything would be okay. I experienced life happening for me, not to me. As I poured into my life, I got back even more.

Within months I was seeing clearer again, though it didn't happen as quickly as it did the first time. The progress was slow, but I respected and honored the work I put in and the progress I made.

I learned the body was giving me pain to warn me, to make me better. The more I avoided or pacified it, the worse I became. I wouldn't have energy or a clear mind; I worked harder and got nowhere; I had no money and had to fake confidence and mask my true feelings about myself. I was drinking alcohol and used many diverting mechanisms that kept people away from me.

I learned the world we live in is not set up to allow us to reach our best selves. It stands on division and needing to be a certain way to be right. I needed to find my way so my body and mind could blossom, expand to a place where I could do less and make more.

After seven years of pain in the massage business, I was at my lowest point, and the Live Pain-Free processes were born. Now I help others do what they always thought was impossible. I help them reach more of their potential. Getting them to feel sexier in their skin, regaining confidence as a mother and as a business woman, making them hyper productive in both areas. In this state pains diminish inside the body, Mentally becoming clearer and more decisive and more importantly they nurture yourselves without guilt. All from my personal experiences and challenges.

Introduction

Stop

Yes, You...

Read this before you begin the book!

You picked up this book because there is a part of you that knows deep down there is more inside, but you cannot get it out. You are working twelve-hour days believing the work will make it possible to be with your family. You are fighting an uphill battle, and it is exhausting you. The money is not where you want it, time is nonexistent, you are always on the brink of overwhelm, and you are fighting to keep a smile on your face for your family's sake.

The kids want more from you, and you can barely keep it together. Your spouse is looking at you, and you wonder if they wish for the younger, more energized version of you.

You run through a rabbit hole of thinking,

"If I just had more time."

"I just do not understand what to do to make them happy."

If I just had a minute to myself, I would be okay."

If I did not have this physical pain and had more energy, I would be so different."

You have been ignoring yourself because you honestly do not know what to do with it. You have attempted so many times to relieve the mental overwhelm, emotional distress and the physical pain to reach a happier, more excited version of you, but nothing seems to work. You've gone through the traditional route of doctor's meds and waiting. You might have even crossed over unwillingly to try Eastern medicine. Though it did not make logical sense to you and you wondered, "How can energy and needles and roots help me?" you heard that it has worked for others.

You might be in the mental overwhelm category or emotional distress world. You have gone to gurus in different modalities, seen different types of therapists, who have given you tests and exercises, and used hacks that worked for friends with similar problems. You think, "If it worked for them, then it might work for me."

If you look deep down, there are feelings of hope and despair, not faith— faith that your body can do more, understanding that you are able to do whatever you see, whatever you put your mind toward.

My clients have told me they feel like they have two choices: spend hours doing self-care activities to stop the pain, or go to a therapist or chiropractors and spend time and money. And they do all this just so they can continue the rat race and make the money they need to live, only feeling good but never feeling their best.

These emotional highs and lows wreak havoc on your life with your loved ones. Your body feels drained, and you don't feel happy in your skin. Sleep habits get worse, and there is no stopping any of it.

If you are completely honest, you are probably trying to figure out an external cause to your discomfort: your pillows, your bed, work, too much to do, no time. The blame game, My husbands has to change first, Client just don't sign up. Kids never do what I want them to.

It has become the norm, and you have now masked it until it becomes so severe you have no choice. You have gotten so used to this place, you no longer see what feeling great feels like.

Or you may be lacking natural energy. You experience constant physical tension and worries about what will happen. There is mental overwhelm or emotional distress. There is nothing left in the tank, and you are not able to produce the things you need so your life can open up. You do not show up in a way that makes you proud, the way you need to so you can handle all the responsibilities put upon you.

Your mind is not able to clear because all your focus goes into making more money to create the life you want.

"How do I feel more confident so I can be that person that can make money easily?"

"How can I do that when I don't feel my best?"

"I feel drained, and my body does not move like it used to."

Then you begin to hear the worst phrase ever running through the back of your mind: "I am getting old!" And you wonder, "How do I make it stop?"

You beg for one minute of peace and quiet, but you do not know how to get better. Your body is showing different symptoms, burning sensations or throbbing. Infections pop up and are harder to get rid of.

Mental brain fog and lack of indecisiveness keeps you from taking an action that will truly help. It is so emotionally distressing to be in this position. You are always waiting to feel exposed and having anxiety. You are waiting for something terrible to happen, but at the same time, it is already happening.

So you mask it. You take meds. You live with the thought, "I can manage it."

You drink drinks that give you energy, and you make it through the day as a survival mechanism. You have some pride in saying, "I survived another one."

In this book, you will break that cycle.

The goal is to give you a roadmap to reach the highest capacity you can reach. It will help you have a clear mindset, so you can produce energy to end your pain, get what you want, create that better version of yourself, make the money you deserve, and maximize the free time you know exists.

In this book, I am going to walk you through a process. It is a simple process that starts with being who you are and understanding where your nervous system is. Your nervous system dictates how much you heal and how you think, and it unlocks your capacity to be your best self. Then you can nurture that place. From a nonjudgmental place, you can allow your body and mind to connect and do the impossible.

Then you can start producing energy naturally. And once you understand how to nurture, you will have a clearer mindset, giving you more clarity day to day.

This will allow you to have a pain-free life and show up in a bigger way. You will have all the money you deserve and be in a state that allows you to create and have a deep intimate relationship with your loved ones.

This state allows you to let go, freeing you from all the rights and wrongs that drain you. You will never again feel the need to control everything, because things always work out.

You will learn how to do less and get more. You will learn how to live and move pain-free. Free from guilt of putting yourself first, because by you putting yourself first everyone get more.

It's not your fault this has happened.

We live in a society that conditions us to believe we need immediate, quick results; to react to everything in front of us; to get what we think is right based on what they say is right.

But this only applies when your pain is severe enough. Until then, avoid looking for the real problem; do anything else that works to pacify and quiet the pain.

The truth is, our body is always giving us clues about what it needs, but we throw away all these little sensations that are trying to tell us something. These clues happen to be the clues you need to reach more of your capacity, which will allow you to heal deeply, adapt to the world, and evolve.

Right now we are stuck in a construct that says to act when our back is against the wall. We never see or realize that our body can produce energy and its environment and adapt to anything that comes its way to help us not only survive but thrive in this crazy world.

Because we avoid the issues that make us uncomfortable so well, we do not realize that we are creating our own walls that we cannot scale to become better. We lose control of what we are able and capable of doing.

So our actions become very chaotic, very elusive, never precise.

The solution is to manage and hack into one linear process that governs us at the core level. The better you know how to use this process, the easier it will be to get past your walls and blocks. Getting past any issue will become simple. Developing yourself into a better version of yourself will be natural.

This one linear program is at the core of every human being, so you must only focus on one simple task that rolls into the next.

As we grew up as infants, our superpower was the ability to learn at a geometric rate. We learn in real time, and what we saw became our reality.

So in the beginning as a child, when you felt sensations, based on your intellectual awareness, you decided if they were harmful or not.

As you grew older, you gained beliefs of what those sensations and experiences meant.

These beliefs dictate our thoughts.

Our thoughts dictate our actions.

Our actions become our habits.

Our habits become our values, which in turn become a part of our humanity level.

This is a linear thought, but what we will be walking through is how to take a larger approach to solve our issues. Traditionally you will find the approach to problem-solving to be about hacking into one process or level.

What we will be doing in this book is bouncing between the beliefs you have to give you a clear understanding that they are there and that they dictate your actions.

To multiply the healing effects, all you must do is build and hone your ability to see and feel within your body.

Doing this will stop the limiting beliefs that dictate the self-sabotaging behaviors that dictate us as adults.

These limiting beliefs are the reason we don't make the money we deserve.

They are the reason we waste time with actions that do not push us to our goals.

They stop us from creating deep relationships.

They keep us in pain. The reason for this is that pain is our body's way of communicating. You have been taught that pain is bad. It is my job now to tell you it is not. Pain is only as bad as the red light in your car that turns on when you need gas.

Pain is simply telling you your gas tank is now low and your warning light is on. You will start to understand that you need a clearer mindset, to stop waiting until that light comes on. This comes as you experience life in its simplicity.

We will do this by having you look at who you are in a nonjudgmental way. Hopefully this sounds better than going to chiropractors and doctors, taking meds, or killing hours at a time doing self-care.

If this sounds worse, please put down the book, because this is how you end pain, get energy, and have a life like a rock star—without the drugs.

You will understand where your nervous system is dictating how productive you are, then how you respond to the external world.

You will witness how easy it is to generate natural energy when you understand who you are and where you are because of your awareness of your nervous system.

You will see when you are wasting energy, based on those beliefs that no longer serve you, causing the red light to flash in the first place.

The nine steps I will walk you through will allow you to live pain-free, so you can do more with your life, business, job, or career.

With this knowledge, you can make more money, which gives you more options in life. Living pain-free gives you the power to create more.

So let us release the stress that is holding you back and causing you pain.

Chapter 1

The Only Domino You Need to Focus On

In my beginning, I had the privilege of taking the long route to access my ability to produce at a higher level, heal at a rapid level, and eliminate pain. Starting as a massage therapist in 2000, I always looked at a person's actions as dictated by their pain.

I believed the reason why my clients were in pain was that they did an action repetitively or pushed the body too far. As I grew as a therapist, though, I realized that was not always the truth. Within the years of me doing the long way of treating and getting nowhere, through massage therapy, I got good at talking with the body. This long way gave me the privilege and honor of listening to the body, and I eventually I stopped doing actions to the body expecting great results.

In fact, in light of my new understanding, I came up with a term to stop me from doing it. I called it *poking and hoping*.

Stop treating your body like a machine. The medical world has shown us that the body has parts that can be swapped out and pushed until they break. This is not a sustainable model to follow, especially when we have a body that may have the ability to live well over one hundred years.

Instead we need to begin to listen, adjust, and adapt to the real-time feedback we get from our bodies. Treat your body as an organism. It is learning from you and changes to the environment.

Once you realize that it is critical to focus on your internal environment, like your belief patterns, you will see that beliefs dictate your actions. This is the fastest way to reach your highest capacity, feel the power in your body, and end the pains that drain you, forever. To stop pain is to understand the beliefs that the organism is going through and the actions that will come after.

By the end of this book, you will understand this and have tactical steps to overcome the reason you have pain.

Together we will explore many red flags that I hear while speaking with clients and eliminate them so you can connect with your body, making it past your pain.

Through my years, I have heard statements like:

- "I cannot connect to my body."
- "It is impossible to stay connected all the time."
- "I believe I can get access, but do not think I am doing it right."
- "I do not know how to continue having access."
- "It is not productive to be connected to your body, because it is too hard."
- "My emotions get too big when I feel in my body."
- "It takes too long to get an understanding of it."

All these beliefs are a way to keep you separated from yourself. When you already have moments of having that connection that you need to stay inside your body, the phrase *staying inside your body* is not as hard to understand.

Here is an example. When you are driving in a car at seventy-five miles per hour, you become one with the car. At that moment you do not believe you are two separate things. You become two tangible objects that become one unit.

The same thing goes for the mind and body. You must learn to feel yourself. It is not something you do. It is something you are.

The simple way to get in touch with yourself is not to think that it is a chore. Putting in the time consistently is not counterproductive. It makes you more efficient. A common mistake is to think *efficient* means "fast." In this world, *efficient* means "productive." You will do less and get more because now your mind is able to problem solve anything.

The body's hyperadaptivity will allow you to become flexible. Flexibility is our first goal, but only when there is a connection.

No one starts off connected and flexible in the body, and definitely not flexible in the mind. This shows in the muscle tissues as a feeling of tightness all the time. Your muscles do not bend and contort the way they can when you are not flexible. Inside the mind, you cannot problem solve. Creativity plummets, and you only see straight lines. Life becomes black or white, right or wrong.

The easiest way to get into your body is to do something physical. But understand that the body is speaking in sensations. So when you are doing anything physical, ask yourself a question. What are the sensations? Avoid the knee-jerk reaction to say, "It burns," if you are working out. Get deeper. You want to look for the smaller sensations inside yourself. The easiest, fastest technique that I know to get a person back in their body is a body scan. But instead of looking for pain, because we want to get you away from using pain as your indicator for action, you want to look for tension.

Tension is a slight sensation. Tension gives you the ability to now catch an upward building pressure inside your body. Using tension as your indicator for an issue is critical. It breaks the habit of waiting until something cannot compensate any longer and breaks.

With this exercise of doing body scans, you can bring them everywhere you go. No tools are needed, and no one will ever know you are doing it.

You can bring a body scan into your morning routine. Do it while you wash the dishes or drive your car. It is something so simple that only takes a minute. Wherever you are, all you must do is look at the tension in your body and acknowledge it. This is how simple it is to bring back awareness to your body.

While washing the dishes, feel the water on your hands. Notice if you are grabbing the dishes harder than needed. Are you white knuckling the steering wheel as you drive? When you are standing in line at the supermarket, look at the tension inside your feet.

At first you may not know what to look for when scanning for tension. I have an exercise or guided meditation you can do to help with this. In this exercise, we will create a cue for your body to release tension. It will be in the form of a light switch.

Imagine a light switch. You know what it does when the switch is pointed up: there is power flowing through the switch, turning on a light. When the switch is down, it turns power off.

Take a second or so and imagine a light switch with your eyes closed. Make it as real as possible; even flick it up and down in your mind's eye. It's imaginary, so there is no right or wrong here. Take a minute now and create that image.

Get in a comfortable position and focus on your breath. Is it fast or slow?

Does it bring up your belly first or your chest? We are observing, so no need to correct it. Sit, watching for a few cycles of breathing.

In your mind's eye, not with your physical eyes, look at your feet. This works better with your eyes closed, but it does still work as you read. Pause until you get a sensation.

Feel your feet, wait until you get a sensation, and then turn off the light switch.

This is literal. Feel your feet, and imagine that light switch you created and turn it to the off position. Bring your awareness back to your feet.

Any different sensation that you get inside your feet is you turning off and lowering the tension.

Take that light switch with you everywhere you go. Sit down, watch an area, and then turn off the light switch. Experience what happens next. Feel what happens inside your body before you turn the light switch on and off.

With some practice, after the light switch goes off, you will start seeing sensations more. And then it is a matter of bringing this into your daily practice.

If you are a meditator, start this before your meditations. Start from your feet and work all the way up to your eyes. This is one of the exercises I did to heal my eyes. I was dumbfounded to feel how much tension I was holding around my eyes.

I had to get comfortable with turning off the tension around my eyes as I was constantly attempting to see the world. As I caught onto when the tension would build, I used the tension as a guide to notice when my nervous system was not in a healing place. More tension around my eyes told me I had to stop and relax for a minute.

I was able to start realizing why that tension returned. I started to learn more and more about the beliefs and why I could not see myself being better—having a full practice and making the money I needed to support my growing family.

looked at why I did the things that did not serve me. I was not able to see the actions I was doing. I never put in the time to see a clear plan to get myself moving further than a few feet.

All were issues I needed to see to access more of my capacity.

The more I started seeing, the more I realized those beliefs and how I was reacting were not by accident. This was a form and a result of my body protecting itself. This realization made my vision clearer.

Do you see, in this real-life moment of mine, how me not seeing the world clearly ended with me rushing through and never planning a course of action that served me? As I began to feel that tension build behind my eyes and I started to take that minute to

turn it off, I was able to stop and see a course of action that created a better result for me. Now when I say a minute, I want you to take a literal minute when you feel that tension.

Let us practice.

In a seated position, take a note of where your feet are. What do they feel like? What are the other sensations? Are they tingling? Are they warm? Are they cold?

Do they feel heavy, or do they feel light? Is there pressure building inside, or are they airy? Now turn off the light switch.

Wait for a moment.

See how your body changes. Feel the sensations that are happening.

Bring that awareness up to your calves. Take note first. Then when you get a feeling of your calf, turn off that light switch.

Bring your awareness up to your knees. Take a glance and become aware of what they feel like. Turn off the light switch.

Move up to the fronts and back of your legs, your quads, and your hamstrings. Is there more tension in the front than the back? Turn off that light switch.

Move up to your hips. Look at your pelvic floor, where your sit bones are. Become aware of your rectum. Is it pulled tightly away from the seat? Turn off that light switch. Become aware of the amount of tension on the outside of your hips. Look at it, feel it, become hyperaware of your hips. Turn off the light switch.

At this point when I am guiding clients through this exercise, I notice them take a deep breath. As you begin to power down, the body responds differently.

Look at how your abdomen is working with your chest. Take note of your level of breath. Is your chest rising a lot, or are you breathing in shallow spurts? Turn off the light switch. See what happens in your belly. See how your breathing cadence slows down or deepens.

Moving to your shoulders, become aware of the sensations there. Turn off the light switch.

Look throughout your arms, elbows, and hands. Turn off the light switch. Do you feel the blood flowing down into your hands now? Was there a temperature change? What sensation was different?

Look at your neck; check in with the sensation. Turn the light switch off.

Scan the lower part of the face, jaw, and tongue. Feel the sensation. Turn off the light switch.

At this point you might feel a line of tightness from your jaw up. If you have vision issues, here is your final coup de grace. Close your eyes and feel that pressure circling the eyeball and the sinus cavity. Turn off the light switch.

The eyes are the windows to the soul. Our eyes have a way of allowing us to see what is literally in front of us in the present and the intangible future self and past experiences.

Many of my clients never experienced how much tension they hold in their face and around their eyes. Releasing it is a way to keep that youthful look.

We are protecting so much; we hold so much tension there. Look and be curious about what you have done internally. How is this different than when you first started?

This feeling you just witnessed, imagine what it would be like to feel like this. Your problem-solving capability is much faster. Responding from this place is productive and efficient. This is what you are capable of. This is how you make strides past your walls.

This is the state we need to be in to begin to understand and rewire the beliefs that are dictating our actions. Let us begin to set up more wins, making you show up bigger. When you are connected and/or have done a body scan, you will begin to see how much of a rechargeable battery you are.

Recap: Feeling compressed and holding tension stops you from performing at a higher level. They limit you to doing the same actions that are not making you happy. A body scan identifies when and where you are holding tension that drains your energy and stops you from being able to think of ways to generate more money or work with a client to reach their goals.

By adding in a body scan, you will be able to do the following:

- Calm yourself down in tough situations

- Turn your mind back on after it has gone into a fight-or-flight response

- Have the energy to restore so you can do more
-
- Have more ways to identify the root cause of why you aren't producing at a high level.

Take action: Do a body scan now if you did not do one already. Experience the sensations of the body as well as clarity of thought and boost in natural energy after.

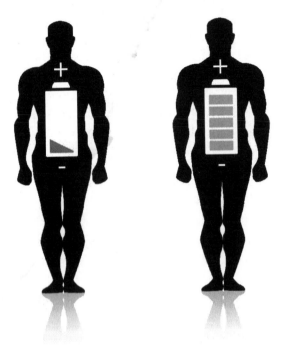

Chapter 2

Be the Energizer Bunny

The average human at rest produces 100 watts of power inside them. This equates to burning around 1,500 to 2,000 calories, or enough energy to power a light bulb. That is at rest. As we start moving our muscles, we can generate from 100 watts to 2,000 watts, which means we need to consume more food for fuel. That is why there are so many different aspects of weight loss. How you move will determine how much you lose. Once you see and understand that you have the capability to produce your own energy, you will change the way you think about food and being low on energy.

The beliefs that I see holding clients back are as follows:

- Not knowing that they can produce energy naturally
- Thinking they must eat to get energy
- Thinking energy comes from external sources
- Not believing or understanding that energy is a real thing
- Believing what they put in, they will get out

Your body needs to produce its own energy to work with the heart and all the organs, but our society teaches us that we need to do all the work to our bodies. At least in the Western world, we have to have tangible proof for us to believe something to be real.

Most of us believe you must put food in your mouth to generate energy. This includes the sports drinks, the energy drinks, coffee, all the things that stimulate the body. Do you believe you need those to produce energy?

The truth is, you don't, and understanding how to tap into the energy-creating part of the organism is our goal. The body already knows how to do this, so we must do the bare minimum to access it. A common statement you will hear me say in this book is, "Less is more." Less is more because the less you mess with your organism, the more it will be able to do.

Then you get to reap the benefits: an abundance of energy with a clear mindset and a clearer thought process. Problem-solving becomes simple, because now your body has the energy it needs. All you have to do is make small tweaks to your daily life. Those little things come in the form of how you move.

How well you move is a key component in getting your energy production back, which means you must tap into and connect with your muscle tissue. The more you can get your muscle tissues to work more efficiently, more productively, the more energy your body will produce with every single movement.

In our world today, we do more things in front of us than behind us, which means the front part of our body is way stronger than the back part of our body by habit.

The more technical way of saying this is our anterior chain has more power than the posterior chain. That makes the human organism off balance.

The balance from front to back is important, and because we do more things in front of us, we create a forward-rounding position. The forward-rounding position alters you physically, mentally, and emotionally.

Physically, it makes your body move in ways that harm the joints, changing the natural movement patterns. This posture affects you emotionally. It puts your body in a position that keeps it in a protective state. This triggers your mind to fire different emotional areas of the brain. More depressive areas fire up when this muscle tissues stay on.

This is where many chronic energy drains originate, the imbalance of front to back, which is not always seen easily. The dominant muscles you use the most daily can cause this imbalance.

Think about any person that has any emotional stress or is physically in danger. The body has hardwired protective mechanisms to protect the soft part of the body. This protective action rolls you forward and changes you in the mind as well.

This is a time accumulation game, which simplifies how you offset the anterior chain's dominance. Think about how often you live your life and work the muscles in the front of your body. You need to offset that by challenging the posterior muscle twice as much.

The easy solve for this is to start working your posterior chain daily. When you work out, make sure you do more exercise for the back part of your body.

The better and more strategically you can get the bigger muscles in the back of the body to turn on and stay on, the more you will produce natural energy.

Here is an exercise that balances the mind and will get the back part of you body to become more function.

Close to a wall at first and done with a hold at first.

Back straight with no arching spine. Bring your opposite leg and opposite arm together behind you. It will feel like a bow with the

sting being pulled back. The opposite arm reaches behind you and grab the opposite heel. Keep the chest up and no arching. Many muscles will turn on to do this activity. The less bend you have in your knee the more challenging this becomes.

This will be held just for 3 seconds. Then switch sides. Once you get a handle of this you can alternate just tapping the heel for 1 minute.

Another exercise is a simple but more challenging for all my walkers. On a good walking surface. A track or a flat surface and walk the track backward. Do a full stride with your legs and pump your arms. This will bring up your heart rate and get all the muscles in the back of your body fired up. Take it at your own pace. You need to feel comfortable walking the track backward to be able to pick up your pace.

Looking for a quick injection of energy? Foam roll calves and your soleus (the muscle underneath your big calf in the lower leg). The reason this works to give you energy is because when the calf in the back of the leg becomes tight, it does not pump blood back up to the heart well enough. The blood pools in the legs and does not have the ability to move back up.

Getting the calves and ankles to open back up helps the blood pump back up to the heart with every step. It also allows you to open your gait, so you can walk faster, more efficiently. This allows you to move through your world way faster.

Foam rolling properly is the key here. Moving slowly and not creating pain. Getting a positive response from your body by having it feel like a melting feeling. If you are poking and hoping, you will make your body protect—the exact opposite of what we are looking for.

Poking and forcing the body to do something will get a change, but it will not change for the long term. We are playing the long game. When you think about energy production, what you do daily in small little bites will produce energy later on its own.

Natural constant energy production is one of the easiest things that you need to shift. It is a matter of shifting your workouts and adding more posterior chain work daily.

Another thing you need to be aware of is areas that are binding and muscles that are not functioning.

There are three things every muscle needs to perform well. One is the ability to move well within the fascia. You need to address the lack of motion using foam rolling.

Two, your muscle system needs to contract well. You address that by using trigger point therapy, which unlocks the muscle fibers that are holding on.

Three, your muscles need to communicate. You will get them to communicate using stretching.

If you are foam rolling your body already, you are ahead of the game. Bringing in the other two is critical for muscle tissue to function properly. Many people do things like yoga or a stretching routine. Rule of thumb: foam roll everywhere to trigger many areas in the posterior chain. Follow this with stretching more areas in the anterior chain.

One of the main areas I have trace into many pains and injuries is the quadriceps. This is the big muscle in front of the leg above your knee. And easy wat to stretches the is to stand tall in front of your bed. Facing away from the bed, giving yourself a little separation between the bed and yourself. Reach back and rest the top of your foot on the bed. As your knee bends and you are standing tall you will begin to feel a stretch. The sweet spot is

standing tall and not feeling much stretch at all. When you begin to squat down now you feel the stretch move through your leg. We will cover more about the importance of feeling stretches move through your body in a later chapter.

Everyone needs a customized routine. We all have our own patterns we need to address. But following the broad ideas above, you will be able to generate energy naturally.

Becoming a rechargeable battery

Recap:

Movement is the key to making energy naturally.

- Get the front part of your body to open by stretching.
- Activate the posterior back muscles using trigger point therapy and foam rolling.
- The more major muscles you can work out and get stronger in the back, the more your body will straighten out.

Straightening out your body will give your mind a boost of clarity, allow you to become creative, turn on the positive areas of the brain, and give you forward thoughts, the thoughts that allow you to manifest the money you want.

Chapter 3

Filling the Black Holes That Drain Us

The two previous chapters were about getting you to connect to yourself to gain access to your energy production while reducing your pain. But you also need to stop losing your precious energy to energy drains. Are you clear on where your energy is going?

Being a super parent while running a business has many moving parts: stressors from normal everyday tasks; children's demands, spousal connection, and relationship building; clients, admin work, employees, and all the delegation.

There are a lot of areas that can drain you. The common thought clients give me with an eye roll is, "My to-do list is endless."

We are here to get you to your highest capability, but we are not talking about clearing your to-do list.

Filling the black holes that drain you is all about looking deeper, looking at the issues that pop up mentally and emotionally and effect you physically.

The beliefs I run into here are as follows:

- "I actively avoid the things that are hard."

- "I must worry to act."

- "I act on things based on avoiding the negative outcome."

- "Black holes and drains are a part of life.

A lot of this boils down to one thing: stress. Within my practice, I have a definition of stress: *Stress* is anything you allow into your energetic space that you allow to affect you.

Everything and anything can be stressors. Music will be okay for one person, but stress out another one.

The heat from the sun will affect a person with dark skin differently than a person with light skin.

We often do not realize that everything is energy; anything can drain us. The love of a parent's life and the common complaint of a parent are the kids; they can be overwhelming. If you have two or more kids, that stress doubles. Work can also be overwhelming with the infamous endless to-do list, clients, bosses, bills, and I can go on. These are black holes; they have a pull on you that takes control of you.

Black holes can be anything. The person experiencing the stress gives it the power. The goal here is to break the cycle of thinking stress is a bunch of tasks we must do.

Stress is anything that you allow in your energy and allow to affect you. You have to deal with the areas in your life that you have deep feelings over. The mistake many of my clients make is thinking there is some big end-all, be-all thing they can fix to end all their stress. The truth is that you have to start with the small things.

I had a client that felt very held down in her position. She put so much energy into it. "This is a man's world, and I am swimming with the sharks," she told me.

While there was truth in what she felt, all she needed to focus on was what she could control. Once she got connected and started generating energy, she began to think better than those men, giving her an advantage she needed.

She started to think of the men as children fighting for a place they were scared to lose. As she gained more clarity, she was able to predict which shark was not doing well and address it before it became a problem.

Get into the habit of finding out the things that drain your energy. Start with the little things first, like how hydrated you are, how much sleep you can get, the timing of your meals, how much touch you need from your spouse, or your need to have a real conversation with a likeminded adult that is not about kids or work. As you begin to stop the little drains, you will have enough power to deal with the bigger ones.

Think about how you are being drained and the beliefs you have that are making it hard to stop.

Maybe you believe you must worry to feel in control of your issue, or even to focus and act. This means you are being propelled by negativity. Here is a clear example of this in something we all do every day: procrastinate. When you procrastinate, you build that worry and pressure so much that you must act. This is reactionary

and never gives us great results. It also takes way much more energy to produce in this state.

Another sensation and emotion we know too well is anxiety. Anxiety will build, giving us this feeling inside that will either make us move or cause us to freeze. The longer you do not do the action, the bigger the stress. The bigger the stress, the more you feel the issue is worth doing something about. Does that sound like one of those cultural constructs I mentioned? We are conditioned to do this to ourselves.

Being anxious is not a necessity of life. Thinking that you need to have some type of stress in life is not beneficial. Granted, there is truth behind needing to stress the body for it to get stronger, but we do not have to drain our energy. Just because we live life, it does not mean it needs to be hard. Remember, life happens for us, not to us. We are at a place where rearranging our priorities needs to happen. Coming from a positive standpoint will give us control back over our world.

We must get to a place where we are consistently doing things that actively bring pleasure to us. As you do this, along with the other tips in this book, watch as harder things become easy.

As you begin to address your emotional side as well as your physical pains, your mind and body begin to do magical things. Their performance enhances by leaps and bounds.

Why would a person need to make something hard for them to learn it?

Take, for instance, sales. Why does a sales process have to be so hard for you to learn it? Why can't it be natural, as simple as building energy, as simple as connecting with your body?

The same goes for love. We see this deep need as daunting, when it is quite easy when you look at it from a new perspective.

It is growth.

So every time you see something that drains you. View it as a mirror image of what you need to do. This is something that can build you up.

Ask yourself why it is draining to you.

What do you have to do?

How is your body responding to it?

Once you figure out how your body's responding to it, it becomes simple to heal. Once you find out that belief, the reason you keep having this issue also ends.

Take the beliefs of needing to worry about finances, needing to worry about being right or proving yourself. Ask yourself, why is that important? Then work the rabbit hole backward.

Proving yourself is one I see often. Being always on, in work and your family life is exhausting on it own. But adding the fuel of proving you are a good mother and producing more money will surely make your body burn out quickly.

Getting to the root of that will save you a massive amount of energy and making being you simple.

Once you understand that, you are in what is called a *boss mindset*. You understand *why* you are doing the actions you are doing, and this allows you to stop doing things that aren't conducive to your goals.

So how do you get to this place of seeing and understanding the drains as well as the beliefs that keep your drains active and present?

First you need to identify when you are being drained. Then you need to sit with it as your mind and body figure out a new routine.

The way to do this is to perform the body scan and see where the locks are inside your body. When you bring up a belief or black hole, look inside your body with your mind's eye. Locate where there is more tension. Is it in your chest? Is it in your gut, or is in your throat? Is it in your jaws, or is it in your hands?

Everything your body says to you has its own meaning, its own dialect.

Remember, we are talking tension, not pain. When your hands get tight, it means you are trying to handle things, trying to hold onto your position or thought process.

So if you are thinking, "I need to be better," and your hands tighten up, that means there is a good chance you have a thought or image of what better is and you are not living up to it. You could be holding onto the position of why you cannot make that image.

It is kind of like a deeper, stronger self is pulling you to what you want, but you are holding onto what you feel is right. This also doubles as your comfort zone.

With this new experience all you must do is watch your hands and notice the tightness. When it comes, you are in a situation that is coming up against your wall. Take that moment and do the scan and turn off the light switch. This will reactivate your body's ability to heal and give you back energy.

Another example I often see that has gone unnoticed in my high-performing clients is tightness in the throat. When this happens, begin the search for something that you must verbalize. Your body's trying to verbalize a hard time or blockage.

Recently I have seen client having trouble speaking up for themselves when it comes to husband affairs. For what ever reason they decide not to speak their mind and emotions.

Show them in that moment look for signs like excessive swallowing, or the need to scratch your face and throat.

Afterwards your throat might feel scratchy. I have seen it go so far as to a slight cough starts to occur. Or a constant need to clear your throat.

If the tightness is in your gut, it is something deep that your body cannot stomach.

So look at your black holes, and reverse them. Think of them as a mirror of a way to acknowledge your body telling you something. Why are your kids bothering you? Why are sales so hard? As you become comfortable with feeling your body, you will notice a time in your sales conversation when your body begins to lock up. You have it in real time now. Turn that light switch off.

It is that simple. Do the body scan. Turn off the light switch and see how your mind and body work. You perform ten times better if you get into the habit of connecting with your body, allowing.

Recap: To regain energy, you must stop the drains on you:

- With nonjudgment, look at yourself and find what is affecting you negatively.
- Think of the mirror. Whatever is bothering you is an area that you need to change.
- Once this feeling is distilled down to an emotion at its root, a logical answer should come to mind.
- Without knowing your circumstance I can give advice on how to fill your holes personally. It is extremely specific to each person, but have faith your mind and body will give you the answer when you identify an issue. That is what they do.
- The starting point to dealing with stress comes down to three things:

  1. Avoiding: Avoiding the stress creates a new pattern around it.
  2. Diverting: When stress comes, focus your attention on the happier side of it, or to a different place internally. Learn how to be around your stressor and experience the opposite perspective. It is powerful but takes practice.
  3. Embracing: Lean into the stressor and figure out all about it and how you are allowing it to affect you. Once you learn everything about your stress, you inherently fall in love with it.

In the moment when I truly understand my enemy, understand him well enough to defeat him, then in that very moment I also love him. I think it's impossible to really understand somebody, what they want, what they believe, and not love them the way they love themselves. And then, in that very moment when I love them . . . I destroy them.

—Orson Scott Card, _Ender's Game_

Chapter 4

Become the Mighty Oak Tree

The oak tree has roots that run deep into the earth. It takes a massive amount of pressure to topple one. We will tap into this strength in ourselves through the concept of getting grounded.

Think of the last time you had a conversation with someone and you wanted to say what was on your mind but did not. Or when, for some reason, all your clients seemed to be draining you. You got into your car and drove home running through the day and how much of a shit show it was. When you walked into the house, the kids and your husband came to greet you, not with love but the problems of the day, and you exploded.

I see this very often. It is plain old overwhelm. This is a sign that you are not grounded.

Being ground is allowing all the energy, good and bad, to travel through you into the earth where it does not harm you.

The first thoughts clients have when I tell them about this concept is, "Do you want me to become a tree hugger, to become airy-fairy and woo-hoo?" This always makes me giggle, but I promise you that is not the case. In fact, most grounded people are the opposite.

Being grounded is being in a place where your mind and body are connected. We are rechargeable batteries and produce energy naturally. That is what we must get connected to. Think about grounding like getting access to the wiring that you cannot see inside of your body.

The goal here is to connect to the wiring inside that is currently shorting out due to the black holes. This shorting out is stopping us from generating energy and allowing the energy to drain from us.

There is a lack of clarity within us. Many believe we have to be a tree hugger and way out there to be spiritual or connected, or that we have to be walls, stoic and full of anger.

This is why you are still fighting for this grounded state. For you to do more with less, you must be grounded. Your wiring inside needs to be flowing positively through you and the negative out of you.

Think free radicals. You are the happiest when you are walking on the beach. The reason why is because the ground is taking all the free radical and negative ions from your body, all without you trying.

It is a matter of allowing your mind and body to work together for energy to flow through you. We focus so much on finding problems and needing it to be hard work to fix them. But instead of fixing them, we actually do the opposite and bind them to us.

Go back to the first step, doing the body scan. Become aware of what triggers you.

This will give you a place from which to start understanding when you are grounded and when you are not grounded. It gives you a place to take the deliberate action that needs to be the practice, the practice of monitoring how your body is working from top to bottom, front to back. It gives you the ability to use your muscles without thinking about it. Then the circuitry inside you can work with ease and grace.

We are taking a micro view on the body for a second now, a day-to-day look. Look at how your body is connecting from front to back, anterior chain to posterior chain, from your feet to your arms. The big disconnect is the upper body connecting to the lower body.

The human body is governed by laws and principles. One principle that plays a huge role here is the principle of *stability versus mobility*. I have used this to identify the root causes of muscular pain.

Stability vs. mobility is the principle that the body flows to keep it safe. Your body will always make the lowest part of your body stable and stiff when there is uncertainty or instability, emotionally as well as physically.

On the physical level it is easier to see than the emotional. Take watching someone learning how to skate on ice. When they first hit the ice, their lower body locks up and their upper body flails in the wind. Your body looks for stability before it gives you mobility, so locking up or becoming ridged is its way of keep us safe.

Think about this when you are attempting to fix your hamstring tightness or wanting to become more flexible. What is the reason for this tightness? What is happening that is making me unstable? Is it that my feet are not stable on the ground? Think about it mentally, physically, and emotionally.

The issue with C-sections is that you need to cut through the abdominal wall, which is a major energetic pathway that communicates between the upper and lower body. In the Eastern philosophy, there are three of these pathways that run from the hips all the way up to your chest. One is a main highway that controls many other functions.

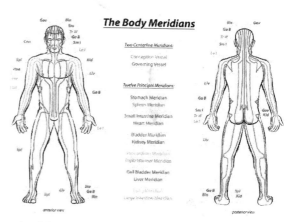

The Body Meridians

Two Centerline Meridians:
Conception Vessel
Governing Vessel

Twelve Principal Meridians:
Stomach Meridian
Spleen Meridian

Small Intestine Meridian
Heart Meridian

Bladder Meridian
Kidney Meridian

Pericardium Meridian
Triple Warmer Meridian

Gall Bladder Meridian
Liver Meridian

Lung Meridian
Large Intestine Meridian

anterior view   posterior view

To be clear, I'm not saying the operation is not important; it has both pros and cons. But what happens after is a person will have trouble syncing up their mind and their body. They will have trouble understanding or feeling what is happening between their lower and upper body and will lack core stability.

Because the process for abdominal contraction has been compromised and the C-section severed those energy pathways, I often have to get the client to relearn abdominal contraction on a physical level.

I see a common emotional thing happen as well. I see a harder time attaching and detaching from things and moments. They are unaware that they have already detached, until it is too late.

For the woman with a C-section who hurts her back exercising, she does not realize that the specific muscle she needed to use in her core was turned off. She begins to use her back instead, causing it to hurt.

On an emotional side, not having a connection to that area around the scar causes issues as well. Not having an intimate connection and/or a hatred for it will cause your body to protect itself. I will give you one guess what the human body uses to protect itself naturally. It is a substance that creates distance from the outside world and is hard to get rid of:

You guess right: fat.

One of the ways I get clients to balance their weight is to get them to love themselves again. The scar is an area ladies have a love-hate relationship with. Start loving it, and it will become a better, more functional part of you.

If you fall into the C-section category, bring attention to that. I am not demonizing the C-section. That is just what happens when you have a C-section. The energetic pathways are no longer touching. Then an older scar will bind and not allow energy to move through the scar. We must make a conscious thought to bring that together.

Now what does that look like in the world of producing at your highest capacity or becoming uber productive in life and business?

If you are allowing all the bad to flow through and out of you, creativity and productivity will become second nature. Your friends and family will begin to say you are on fire because you are on point now.

A client said to me once she was "kicking ass in the board room and in the bedroom," which makes sense in so many ways. You will have an advantage over most other people.

In the world of grounding, there is a sensation of heaviness, a sensation of emotions centered and clear. The mind is quiet and slow. When you are not grounded, you are reacting to the world. Grounded, you are responding to the world because the fast world will come in slowly.

By practicing small activities daily, like the body scan, you will find that the sensation of heaviness and centeredness will become a marker. It will serve as a signal that gives you the red light or green light for your hard tasks.

This gives you clear markers when you are off, showing you wandered into a hole that is draining your energy.

When you find yourself there, your next action is to reconnect.

The activity here is to feel sensations across the body and down the body. You can do this in many ways. While working out or stretching, can you feel the stretching throughout the muscles? Then can you feel that same stretch influencing other areas of your body?

In the case of the C-section (though you can also do this if you haven't had one), here is a helpful stretch:

1. Take a knee.
2. Project the hips forward, more so on the side with the knee down.
3. Raise the same side arm to the ceiling. "Right knee down, right arms up."
4. Feel the stretch area around the scar.

Do you feel a stretch around the scar? Does it feel like it's binding, not allowing you to feel through the area?

A common binding site is when an area does not allow sensation through it. This where you are binding and no longer allowing energy to flow through.

When this happens, the goal is to get energy to flow through the area using this stretch. This works with any stretching you do. Find a binding site, wait, and breathe:

- Go right until you feel the stretch lightly.
- Bring your awareness to the area outside that stretch sensation. Allow yourself to breathe deeply and slowly.
- The stretch will begin to grow because you are doing it in a safe way.
- Be connected to the area. Don't rush this process.

Your body will start to rewire how it is working, adapting and healing that site. All that those pathways represent will come back online.

If you are successful with this, then you will have scaled one of your walls. A wall is a block, on the physical side as well as mental and emotional. Remember, we are only looking at the body as parts. You are your mind and your body.

Clearing these will assist you in ways you will never know. Because you have rewired the stopped energy flow patterns causing your unwanted behaviors, this will now translate into giving you the ability to do more with less.

Bring these small sensations to light and clear them up within your body. This will give you the creativity and mind clarity to make even more small changes, which will result in you growing exponentially.

I have a mentor that has really shifted my life and given me so much. One of the many things he has burned into mind is this quote: " He would say its not from him but because I heard it from him it is his."

> You can be committed to your results or you can be committed to your reasons. You cannot have both.
> —Ryan Niddle

Doing what you need to do is all that matters, or else you will come up with excuses. Be committed to improving yourself so you can make the money you deserve. I am showing you it is not hard work. It is based on the easy stuff we jump over.

What I am asking you to do is be committed to feeling these small blocks. Do the body scan whenever you choose. Be committed in that moment to connect, find a block, and work with it. When done daily, the amount of energy and changes that will happen will blow your mind.

Recap: Becoming the mighty oak is in reach of all of us. We will have to reach into ourselves and dig deep.

- Take a few moments of your day and look at what is happening. Do that body scan. Are you grounded?
- While doing your stretching activities, see if you are binding.
- When you find areas that are binding, slow down, stretch, and breathe.
- Be sure that as you breathe in and out, the stretch moves with you.
- Keep doing that until you get a stretch to link from top to bottom.
- Done daily, this will clear up emotional resistance and improve connection between your higher self and lower self.

Chapter 5

Not Your Typical Daily Routine

So many people struggle with the thought of having a daily routine.

It is a consistency issue. They say, "I do not have a daily routine. There is too much chaos."

I have also often heard people say, "I have tried to have a daily routine, but I just can't seem to keep it."

The reason why it is easily dropped is that we always want to do what we want to do rather than realizing what is right for us. What is right is not to be determined by me or someone external from you. But if you start to become more connected with your body, you will find a natural communication will emerge. You will have feelings about what you want to do.

You will become clear on the difference between what you need and what you want.

The process you have been following will also open you up to being open to discovering who you are on a deeper level.

The better you understand who you are, which is a book on its own, the more customized you can make your daily routines.

At the beginning of the book, we were clear that you have physical pain that is draining you of energy. If you have no energy, you cannot be mentally clear. This steals your true potential from you.

Some general questions that I get are as follows:

- What does your body need each day?

- How do I know what is right for me?

- Do I have to do the same thing every day?

As you can see, all these questions show a person's uncertainty in who they are.

There is an expectation of needing a routine that is perfect, or else it is not going to work. A perfect routine for each person is a myth. Create the routine that works best for you. Some people need variety.

A perfect example of this is cardio versus lifting weights. Those are the first things you think of when it comes to a good workout routine. But this limits you to two options, when there is more to you than that.

If a person needs to calm their mind and plan, they need an emotional or mental workout. Adding in a mental and emotional routine is valuable. It gives you quiet time and time to journal out your thoughts.

Journaling is another place where I see many getting stuck in the idea that there is only one way to do it. All journaling is about, though, is your emotions or planning. Journaling can be where you can track yourself. When does your body need to work out heavily, and when do you need light movements more? You will discover if you are a morning person or a nighttime person. You will see if you are you conditioned to quiet your mind yourself or need help to.

I will assure you there is not one best routine, but you need to add routines for all of these areas these to your life. You don't have to add them all at once, but having these different types of routines will help you be more healthy, physically, mentally, and emotionally.

The goal here is not to give you another chore to do. It is about tacking onto what you are already doing but getting you to connect first. You must allow your body to build its energy reserve. Find those subtle little blocks with whatever you are doing.

Make that a daily practice.

Shift from a chore-based routine to an achievement feeling. Dive deep into connecting now and how addictive it is.

Think about the sensations of sex. We all love those feelings before, during, and after. What we are craving and attracted to are the sensations. You never think it is a chore when you are feeling those sensations. It is a happy place all on its own. You can lose yourself there.

This is what we are tapping into: the feeling of getting lost in the sensation. It is a shift from willpower and over-thinking, saying things like, "I have to do this routine because it is good for me."

Instead, become curious, wanting to see what sensations are to come. You will know you are doing this when you say, "I wonder what will come up next."

Ask yourself, "How will these new sensations make me better? Will they make me feel so good that I produce more for my family?"

When you change your mindset from thinking of this as chore, to "I get to do this," once it is done, it becomes a sense of achievement, not drain. You become pumped afterward, ready to take on the world, refreshed and excited at the same time.

The easiest thing you can do to set yourself up for success is have something you do for you. A pregame of sorts that builds a better you is our goal.

I have read a lot of self-help books. I was reading about women accessing a deeper level of love. In one of the books, the author spoke of a scenario of a date night. The woman showed up to the man's house an hour early and came into the house to hear the man in the shower. She noticed the door was cracked open, and she could see inside. What she saw changed the way she felt about the man dramatically. She saw him come out of the shower and set the stage. He filed his nails, put rose petals on the bed, sifted through CDs to have good music, and put on a good scent. In that moment, the woman saw that he genuinely cared about what was happening. He put time and effort into the way he looked and felt, and more importantly, how comfortable she felt.

From the standpoint of pregame routines that set the stage for success, this blew my mind. Doing these things daily not only helps you but the people you want to influence. The male was just doing something so natural, and the woman felt loved.

This is what we are looking to develop: a daily routine that sets you up to feel good, but with one tweak. That tweak will add a building component to your routine, developing more energy and healing. These daily activities will start to feed a growth pattern rather than a stagnation pattern.

A stagnation pattern happens so often even with the best of intentions. I see this a lot with the concept of corrective exercises to heal pain, such as hip activation and glute activation exercises. I teach hip presses, to begin a person's connection with their hips. A month down the road, if you are still doing those presses with the same frequency, they did not correct what we needed. There is a disconnect somewhere.

If you are in a world of doing the same thing for hours and you are not seeing progress, that is not correct, and in your mind, it will default to being a chore.

The daily routines that feed you are also going to grow you and make you become a better version of yourself. Further, when something does go awry, the same routine at a lower energy level will begin to fix the area.

The biggest thing you need to remember is that going back to the basics always works. Our basics that we are developing so far are connecting, allowing, and grounding daily.

If you have been following along, you know you should be doing body scans, showing you where you hold most of your tension. As you do the body scans more frequently, you will start connecting with yourself in an intimate manner. You will feel and notice subtle changes that will add up to massive improvements in mind and body, allowing your body to produce more energy, allowing you to produce more throughout your days, and helping you pick up on and clear up the black holes that are stopping and draining you. This will allow you to stop being stressed at any given moment.

Now you have made it through the stage of doing some internal hardwiring reconnection during your daily routines. This should shine a light on your imbalances in your muscle world.

Are you seeing issues like your hips not allowing stretches or energy through them? Do you not feel your feet during a squat?

Are your shoulder always up by your ears, never coming down?

Find those binding sites in that grounded state. Stop and connect with them, rewiring them in real time. Doing this only takes a second or two, but this is where you become committed to your results. This is the tweak that will set you up to grow.

Take the conversation we spoke about earlier. You decide to swallow your words. You feel that slight sensation in your throat. Or you notice you are swallowing more. The fix here is taking that moment and bring it up. Say inside your head or out loud. " I realize I want to say something but for some reason it is not coming out right. Do you mind.

Take a minute feel anything. Your heart rate for example. Become curious about it. It is not good enough to shift the state you are in just by saying I feel it. How fast is it going, rate, texture, is it beating out of your chest? Clients mostly say I don't feel my heart be in that moment. They stop and they can not feel it. This is because your nervous system is to heighten, and you are in a fight or flight response. This is where a break is needed regardless.

Feel your heart and see if you can get a shift just by watching it. This might only take one minute or 5. In that moment when you get your heart to slow. See if your can feel a stretch through your neck. Watching it stretches through that place of tightness.

If successful speak your mind and heard. Start with how you feel in that moment. Followed by asking how he feels in that moment.

Congratulations you have in real time unbound a deep issue your body need to clear.

It is empowering to know you have the ability to stop in the moment and work with your little baby wall and/or a block you have found, by giving it attention and nonjudgmental acknowledgment.

The key here is that when you find stubborn areas that keep popping up in your daily routine, you will need some help with them. Those are the places where you now reach out and say, "Excuse me, therapist/bodyworker/nutritionist, this is where I am getting stuck." This place will be very specific to who you are.

You have now pinpointed your own issue. "I keep showing up in my daily routine, and it feels like _____ (fill in the blank)."

- Always rushing through it just trying to get it done.
- I am not focused making many foolish mistakes
- I can not feel my body durning certain time with my husband.
- When I come around certain friends and family I shut down and feel like I am not able to speak up.

Do you see how this can save you time and money? You are the leader in asking for help, and this is the way it should be. No one knows you better than you. When you follow this path, which is so personal, you should never allow another person to tell you how you feel. Own that space. You may not know how to fix it, but you know how you feel. Be the leader, and this will help you get the answers you want faster. That therapist or healthcare worker will have a much better idea of what to do because of it, saving you time and money.

Whether you do your daily routine in the morning, noon, or night, if you are doing something that feeds who you are, you will start to blossom and grow as a human being.

Before you grow as a parent, before you grow as a salesperson, an entrepreneur, all the work you are doing needs to help you grow within yourself. The only way that will happen is if you are feeding your organism. Your daily routines do that. That is not a chore, but an achievement, something that feeds you.

Other things you can do daily that work as well as the scan

are foam rolling, trigger point therapy, and stretching. I use these three to build body awareness in your muscular system and bring that system back online.

The byproduct of this is clarity in your mind and more sensations in your body. You will be producing and moving deliberately, and your pain will diminish.

And once that happens, the fun part happens. That is when you start to load and start to challenge yourself. But it is not something you think about. It is not something you consciously do. This is where the domino effect will be in your favor.

You will start to challenge yourself because of the safe place you have been working in. You will no longer be in a closed, protective mindset. Curiosity will become a new state of mind. A little voice will say, "I wonder if this will happen," and it will not be a thought, it will be an action you are taking in real time.

This experience will make your mind and body more flexible, allowing you to do way more things because your mind and body are synced. You will be able to take more strategic risks without blowing out because you are always keeping yourself safe.

This is the byproduct of your daily routines.

Recap:

- Accessing the domino effect is the goal.
- The body scan finds tension.
- You want to create a safe place to become curious.
- Safety plus curiosity influences rapid growth.
- Growth from within doubles the output and pressure you can withstand.

Chapter 6

Are You Up for the Challenge?

An elephant is one of the strongest land mammals we have on earth. Imagine if we tied an elephant to a deep stake in the ground to keep the elephant from moving. With little effort, it would rip the stake out of the ground and walk away. But like our minds, it is all based on a belief of perspective.

Carnivals use a method based on the perspective of resistance to tame elephants. As a baby, an elephant meets a stake in the ground. It fights with that stake as hard as it can for as long as it can, but eventually it gives up, exhausted. At first the elephant will begin to struggle and not be able to pull that out the stake. The struggle and energy the baby elephant puts up is not a match for the stake at this young age. At this stage of his life, he does not know his power, nor can he access it. Falling shy of being able to beat the resistance of the stake, he sees the stake as unbeatable and stops trying.

As the elephant grows up in this situation, all it has known in its life is fighting this stake and losing, coming up against the resistance and losing. This results in a strong elephant defaulting to not trying to beat a wall he perceives as unbeatable. As soon as the elephant feels the resistance

of the stake in the ground, he stops. It is a triggered response.

This training process can take weeks to even months to settle in, resulting

in having a grown elephant not ripping out a stake in the ground. This makes the elephant seem tame and weak, when it is not.

That taming process happens to us all, without us even knowing it.

I see this issue often when it comes down to people challenging themselves. They come up against resistance and they stop, because they felt similar resistance before and lost.

Or I see the flip side of the coin: people make the easiest thing harder to feel the fight they have in them. But they still lose, because the stake is unbeatable.

"I saying that I bring up with my client when I see this " you are killing an ant with a sludge hammer using all your might"

The belief is that they need to do something harder than what they are capable of.

This builds the perception that a challenge needs to be met with force or a pressurized nervous system, or else you cannot succeed.

That is where procrastination comes in handy. You build up pressure inside, nervous energy and anxiety, and you come out the gate guns blazing.

Or you have a challenge forced onto you, giving you no choice but to fight your way out.

Shift your mindset and start challenging yourself. Break free from the thought of needing to be thrown into a challenge or procrastinating until the very last minute.

What this looks like in the world today is someone giving you a challenge. If it is big enough and causes you enough pressure inside, then you run with it. If not, you wait, because there is no force to compel you.

Take personal trainers. I'm not knocking the profession; that's how they make a living. But people need them to create that pressure to work out, or they can't do it themselves.

Accountability works better, as someone helps us and walks us through it.

But what happens if we shift that point of view? What if we made your challenge based on your comfort level?

As you start to grow more and more in touch with your daily routine, if that daily routine is inside of your comfort zone rather than something that is given to you, like any muscle, the body will start to adapt and grow with that daily routine.

If you connect with your body, your body will generate energy, no longer being drained of all the extra energy as you clear out the black holes. You keep your circuitry nice and firing together from top to bottom. In your daily routines, whether it is journaling, working out, or any type of movement practice, the natural progression is to start challenging yourself. You'll begin to start wondering, "What if," and you'll start adding on a little bit of a heavier load, without ever thinking twice. You will never do something that you cannot do, because you are listening to your body. And because this is happening daily, you will not even realize that it is any different.

So how do you challenge yourself in a safe way?

If you are doing something daily, you want to have a constant monitor on how well your body is pushing.

An easy metric is saying out loud out on a scale of 1 to 10, with 10 being too much and 1 being too little, where am I pushing my body?

PAIN MEASUREMENT SCALE

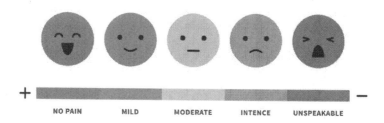

NO PAIN   MILD   MODERATE   INTENCE   UNSPEAKABLE

Two different types of people do their workouts unconsciously. One type only pushes themselves to about a 3 or 4; (just past mild in the illustration above) they go until green, let's say. The other type, on the flip side, will push until they yack, to a 9 or 10. That is orange into red.(just past intense)

As you work and you start doing daily challenges, you want to stay closer to the 5 or 6 level, high yellow going into orange, (moderate slightly into intense) where you are not close to maxing out and falling apart. This is the safe zone where your body can still adapt and grow. We are still pushing harder than we normally would, but the consistency of doing it daily makes it the new norm.

This is where hacking into that one program we spoke about in the beginning of the book comes into play. We have been changing our beliefs, which changes our thoughts, which changes the words we say. Our words change our actions, and our actions, done long enough, turn into habits.

So if you are habitually pushing out a 5 when you do your daily activity, your body's going to want to adapt. It is going to change because it is safe to do so. As you become stronger, it will feel easier to do the same action.

Once that 5 becomes a 4, because you have been doing this from a safe place of feeling accomplishment and the sensation of how you are working, you will naturally ratchet it up without even thinking.

Now you are doing more with less effort.

A great example of this is when you are paying your mortgage. You have thirty-year payment at $2,400. You find out you can get a lower payment of $2,000, and you do.

Yes, the $2,000 is a lower payment, so mentally you relax. Most people fall into that trap. By doing the $2,000 route, you have throttled your needed. This slows down your productivity and liveliness.

The better thing to do is to keep that higher resistance point. We actually are doing this off of feel. We feel the space we just received and noticed it got easier, so we naturally go back to that higher resistance point. Even though the payment is only $2,000, we go back to paying the $2400, and this now allows us to pay down the debt faster and never see a difference in output. We have now become two times as productive without having to actually do more.

It's all about perspective. If you demonize resistance and shy away from it, it becomes bad and feared. By making it safe and staying curious about it, you open up two times as much of yourself.

Become attracted to the sense of accomplishment. That feeling makes you feel good. This will turn into a place of meaning. As you chase down that feeling, it becomes you. You will lead with meaning throughout your life without you noticing you have done anything.

A sense of meaning will trump a want to do every time. As you start to need this sense of accomplishment, it will become a priority. By leaving your body to do what it does best, it starts to evolve.

What does this look like in the real world?

You start doing tasks faster, becoming more and more productive. Family life and chores happen quicker and with less effort. Business becomes clearer in your mind. You learn faster.

As you are being more productive, your curiosity trigger kicks in, and you ask for a bigger load. It is needed to satisfy this thirst to challenge yourself. Your new way of safely challenging yourself will accelerate your growth. Not to mention, this is not based on willpower. This is naturally produced and sustainable energy you are using. At this medium expenditure, you are not going hard all the time, and there are no surprise crashes when the unexpected and guaranteed mishap comes.

How would you like to exponentially accelerate your growth and feel like you have not done anything different?

I believe in this say and say it often to myself: "The universe, your God, your higher power will never give you anything you cannot accomplish, that you are not ready for."

As you do your daily routines at this level 5 looking for the 6, doing this from a connected safe place, your body will start to evolve and grow. You will become more and more in touch with who you are and what you can do based on how you feel.

The world starts to open for you, because everything changes once you feel good inside of yourself.

This example of challenging ourselves daily was based on the physical boy, but the same principle applies to your emotional and mental worlds as well.

Major pitfall warning: This will not work if you lose connection with yourself. You will find resistance and push against resistance, never making progress. This is a dance; as you come up to your walls, you cannot smash through them. That is resistance fighting resistance, the opposite of what I am speaking about here.

Take your time and experience what your body is doing. How it naturally throttles when it needs to and gives you the green light to go.

Recap:

- Find that sweet spot of 5 and stay there.
- Do this daily.
- Track and be aware of the ease of challenge you have set up, and chase down that resistance.
- Watch for the curiousness of adding more load. Beware, it is addictive, and you can add too much to your plate, causing you to push your output to a level that is not sustainable.
- Marvel at how easy your daily tasks become.

Chapter 7

All About the Reps

It is all about the reps.

In the workout world, we all know the higher number of reps you can put up, the stronger you get. The more you challenge the human organism, the better it will adapt, change, and grow.

We are going to work off this model of putting up more reps to get stronger. What I want you to understand is it not the number of reps you can do, it is how you do them.

It is also how much load you put on those reps. For instance, if you were lifting ten pounds, you can go to twenty reps. If you lift thirty pounds, you might be able to go to ten reps. If you go to fifty pounds, it might be three reps. That is the traditional model for working out to get stronger. The higher load tries to get as many reps as possible, but if you can, tax your body and do fewer reps to failure. You will adapt to grow that rep count.

If you have been following this book, you have realized that I have hacked into that model and made your life into reps if you knock over the first domino.

The common failure that I see here is, people never allow their body to bring up their energy naturally. They are too worn out. They are not giving themselves enough time to reenergize so they can produce the energy they need. They can barely do their natural day-to-day activities, let alone add the load of the next stressor.

If you fall into this place of feeling like you don't have enough energy, you need to double back to the filling of the black holes. Find those triggers and quiet them. This is a sign that the nurture side needs to improve within you.

When you start to do more and more reps of this, massive change will occur in your mental and emotional world. This is not forced in this natural model that I am teaching you. If it feels like effort, you will create more turmoil.

The anagram of FEAR, false evidence appearing real, will no longer apply. This is because what we have been doing in this whole book is based on you connecting to yourself, feeling your body, using the infinite wisdom of the body to tell you how much you can push, showing you where you are tight and how your body is responding to the world. As that happens, your body then shifts over to producing energy to balance itself out.

As you start to clear out all the energy drains in it, you start to ground yourself more. You start to produce more energy, feel better, and get grounded, and your internal circuitry works better. You become more efficient, more productive. At this stage, your body is healing and preparing for more efficient work for the next time around.

At this point, you are doing daily routines that are safe. This is where you are now, leaning on that 5 to 6 level, turning up the gas a little, asking for a little more weight
And then you challenge yourself, and you hit a wall. In my head it is like a guard blocking my way. I must not only have the confidence to stand there in front of him, but I must speak with that

same manner, BECAUSE I KNOW I OWN THIS PLACE. Literally, it is my head. In this world we have created, we are hitting walls of our own creation.

These walls are in the daily activities we do: feeling the stretch in one spot that is stuck, stopping to breathe, and watching the body open.

The wall is emotionally looking at those triggers that drain you, getting up out of bed and doing the daily routines, and defining your level 5 to 6 and staying there in all areas of your life.

This whole time you have been chasing down walls. As you do this more and more, it will become easy. Then the walls you chase will be bigger and have more magnitude to impact your life. You will climb them and smash them down.

As this process happens more often, you will recognize a smaller wall, and you will smile when you see it coming.

You will no longer fear that wall. You will know there is a better version of you on the other side, and you want to meet that person.

The reason I know you will want to meet this person is because I see it all the time in the practice. Once that curiosity bug takes hold, you will always want to be the better version. It is conditioned inside this process we are doing. Once you knock down that first domino, you are along for a ride. The daily tasks of you challenging yourself give you the confidence needed to be able to scale that wall. It's that simple.

You can now push yourself and come up against the wall, no longer scared because it is just a rep that you are coming up against, a challenge that you now put in front of your face. And it is in a safe world, your safe world that you created. Once your body is grounded and connected, it has fewer energy drains and is producing energy.

A bigger system kicks in: the nervous system. As the nervous system does not have to be in a heightened protective state, it changes many functions in the body. It will drop down, giving you the ability to adapt.

The problem-solving part of the brain comes back online. The actions you do change, giving you a better result, if you keep following the connection of your body.

The easiest way to practice coming up against the fear is to practice coming up to your challenge in a daily activity at a 6 to 7. This means physically as well as emotionally.

Try this doing a daily activity that you know you dislike a little bit, like taking a cold shower. This is one of the exercises that I teach my clients to break past. Do it so often that the impossible becomes possible.

Let's practice coming up to fear in a safe place using this cold shower.

Start by having a nice warm shower and washing yourself off.

Then do three reps of a cold shower.

Let's start at an 8 out of 10 on a hot scale, where your shower temperature is at 80 percent of the temperature you can stand.

Then bring that down to a 5, or 50 percent.

It will be shocking almost. I want you to breathe and learn to be at ease at this temperature. Begin with 30 sec to a minute. the longer

you can do this the better no need to do longer then 3 minutes for this purpose of learning to come up to fear.

Then I want you to bring it back up to 80 percent.

Here, the water will start to feel warm, bordering on hot.

Take a few breaths there knowing that you are going to be bringing it down to 40 percent.

Here you know the shock will be even more. That is the practice, that is the rep against coming against fear.

Bring it down to 40.

Breathe. Notice, connect with yourself, and feel that your body is going into that shock and panic.

Learn to bring yourself out of that shock so you can breathe and adapt.

On the third rep of this go for your personal best of cold.

Watch how your body gives you different sensations in that fear state even before you enter the cold water. Watch how your mind moves faster. Your body trembles slightly. You have this urge to turn off the shower and end it.

When you do come outside of the shower, you will have built a deeper relationship with your body.

We are not talking about doing reps to waste time. We are not talking about needing much time to do any activity. The amount of time needed to do your self-care will go down the better you are at coming up to your wall.

Spending hours and hours or tons of money going to doctors that also take hours of your time will be a thing of the past.

If you are doing the things in this book daily, you are doing things that will help you grow. And as you knock over those few first dominoes, something magical will begin to happen. You will reclaim your time.

You will use your housecleaning time as time you are feeling you muscles work harder than before. Business calls will become more connected because you are stretching your emotional muscle.

Chapter 8

No Need to Fake It Till You Make It

There is no need to fake it till you make it. Confidence is something that everyone wants and drives for, but most do not realize what is required to become confident.

Confidence is not an elaborate, tangible thing you get. Confidence is something you become.

Everyone has a way to deal with competition. They normally find some way to pump themselves up, with different music, chemicals, drinks, and stimulants like coffee to get that energy boost they need to act on the pressure building. This is a form of willpower, and willpower is fleeting and is not always available.

Confidence is based on your mojo.

You need to start realizing that as you start to do these daily routines, start challenging yourself in this way, and start scaling your walls, there is no need to fake it till you make it.

Your level of confidence will become natural. You won't need willpower, which burns twice as much energy. You are now practicing reaching down and accessing energy on a daily basis.

Confidence has a foundation in discipline. Discipline comes from daily action done over time. Where people fall apart is when confidence is not tangible and there is no tangible metric to rate it.

In this book we always start with our feeling. Our body's feeling gives us the metric we need to judge where we are. When we see what is happening in our body, then we can start to see just how much more energy we can feel.

Even if you are an introvert that needs to be an extrovert for something like a conference or holding a seminar, you now know how to build energy naturally, and it is still safe because you designed it.

Remember, you create your world. Your universe, your God, your higher self is never going to give you more than you can do. The key is to get exposed to this new level of being confident.

n the earlier chapters, we talked about daily routines and challenging and putting in a rep. This rep is you coming out of your comfort zone.

This is you experiencing something that is uncomfortable and close to your breaking point. That is when you are pushing your challenge up to the 7 or 8 based on curiosity. Based on that "I wonder" statement.

You feel safe and you can adapt; you are able to push your muscles through that action. At this stage accomplishment is not the goal, exposure is. Expose yourself to a place of confidence.

Mirror someone who is confident.

What we are doing now is living with confidence, not because we willpower it, but because we manufacture it, based on our daily routine. That is now a sense of accomplishment. As you do that more and more, your level of competence in whatever area you are playing with will skyrocket.

Here is an exercise to do to build an understanding of how easy it is to gain confidence:

Take a handball or racquetball and sit in a chair facing a wall.

From two feet away from the wall, bounce the ball for the first time. When you see where the ball hits the floor, draw an X, as well as where the ball hits the wall.

This is different for everybody.

Then keep throwing the ball and watch where the ball hits, repeatedly. Make sure you are bouncing the ball and hitting the X every time.

Once you see you are speeding up, then step back from where you are.

Throw the ball at the X on the floor and watch how you naturally hit the X on the wall and now catch the ball with speed.

As you get more comfortable, you will hear those words: "I wonder . . ."

"I wonder if it will happen every single time." "I wonder if I step back, if it will do the same thing." You will instantly try to challenge yourself because you feel confident in doing something. By doing something daily or routinely and in this case in the same manner, we are now applying hat same principle to life. Once it is simple, you become confident. Once you are confident, the world opens.

Shadow someone who is confident. Walk and talk like them. Don't become them; just get a feeling of what it is like to feel confident. Practice what that would look like in your own words and style. As you practice that in your world, you instantly become that confident person in the eye of your client. You show up differently, which shows leadership, and people want to be led.

Chapter 9

Let It Go

If I want to see a funny face on any one of my clients that is trying to reach a goal, I tell them to let it go. Once you make the goal, write it down, prep, and show up daily. You then have to not focus on it—just put it out to the universe.

They say, "After all you taught me? How to control every aspect of my day, how to work less and get more based on monitoring the sensations in my body? Listen to what you are saying. Now that I have the goal and have the practice, you want me to be unattached to the outcome?"

One hundred percent of the time, I see fear fall onto their face. Most of the people I work with are hyper attached. They need to control every aspect to get what they want, to get what they think they need.

Many people believe that the effort you put in the entire time you are involved in the activity will get you the outcome you need it. It is such a habit to push harder.

Now it is true that pushing harder will get you the outcome sometimes.

But it is not going to get you there 100 percent of the time. Pushing harder does not mean you are going to get your goal, but it will ensure you burn through most of your energy rapidly.

What we must do is learn how to detach ourselves, as fearful as it is. We must relinquish control and understand that based on your faith, your universe, your God will never give you something you cannot do. Your control comes from who you are and how resourceful you are with what you have.

When you push, you only create tunnel vision and compress your mind and body. Your nervous system elevates, putting you into a fight-or-flight state, and turns down your ability to heal rapidly and adapt. Once this happens you begin to react to the world.

Pushing harder pushes you out of a grounded state. It causes you to crash, burn out, feel like you are not good enough. This leads you to not hitting your goals and feeling overwhelmed about daily life and business.

So stay grounded and connected and produce a sustainable amount of energy, where you can handle what the universe throws at you. You will begin to open up life for you instead of having it come crashing down on you. What needs to happen for you to live a life you want to live will appear. The help you need, a mentor or nanny, a good hug from a person you have not seen in a while will be right on time, all by design, making you the best human you can become.

This is not all about blowing smoke up your butt. Life is not sunshine and roses. There are times things will not work out the way you want. When this happens to me, deep down in my heart, I say, "It's because that's what needed to happen for me to learn the lesson."

These lessons will keep happening until you get it. If you are getting what you need to progress as a human, you will repeat it again somewhere else in your life.

Take, for instance, a situation with your boss or a client where you did not say what you were really feeling about an issue. Then it happens again in a fight with your spouse. All you needed to do was say what you were feeling.

This is so common, and because a person is not connected, they repeat this lesson, stalling progress, keeping them spinning their tires in their pursuit of happiness.

How many times have you made the same mistake repeatedly? That is because you were not in a place of balance.

You were hyperattached to the result—proving a point, not feeling taken advantage of, attempting to get the most out of the situation right at that moment—forgetting this is life filled with many opportunities that are coming toward you.

In some ways because the universe is guiding it, it already has happened.

We must be able to be flexible, mentally, physically, and emotionally. We must learn to let things go because it is always going to work out for our best good.

As we are always working out every day, challenging ourselves every day, there will be little that our universe brings to us that we cannot handle. The fact that we keep on asking for more and more challenges makes us stronger by the day.

To make this simple, all you must do is stay true to the number one domino.

That one domino will save you headaches and gray hair. You won't need to have multiple hands and a head that swivels seeing all things always. That one domino gives your mind and your body the permission to do what it does best.

It heals adapts, grows, and spreads its love.

When your mind and body feel safe, their natural hardwiring will kick in every time. Create that safety. That is the only thing you need to do, which is why it is so simple to heal. Bring your body and your mind back together. Doing this breaks the traditional model of you being different parts and needing to fix the symptom. But it has infinitely more benefits for your mind and body, allowing you to become hyperproductive.

The reason this is so hard is that the constructs around you, the world we live in, the way our society perceives what is right, cannot allow you to be functional.

Science has conditioned us to look for tangible proof. This dictates the medical world. The medical world has made things simple and fast, healing on demand, which makes it convenient for our culture to run off with.

That's not to say we don't need it, but what has happened is you have forgotten what you are made of, what you are capable of doing. Bringing this back is your ultimate goal.

After reading this book, I hope you begin to realize that goal and start taking these small steps. You do not need to make it complicated and drawn out. You don't need fancy tools to get what you want or to take the quick fix while dreading the aftereffects. You are an organism that will get there if you work with yourself properly. You are right where you want to be by doing what you need to based on who you are.

To sum all this up, you will start to learn to understand who you are because you are looking at simple signs your body and mind are giving you. Once you understand who you are, you begin to only do what you need to do, to create moments where you can have your cake and eat it too.

No more running out of time, but creating more time. As you are creating more time, you can push at a rate that is faster than most and sustainable because it is not your limit. To make this realistic, you will need to create the boundaries you need to keep you safe.

Think of crabs in a bucket. As one crab begins to change its ways and make progress climbing up the bucket, another crab grabs its leg and pulls it down. It is common and expected that everyone is trying to make their way out of the bucket.

As you begin to find your way to your better self, another will challenge you or not like that you are changing the dynamics of what was normal. Expect this and create boundaries to keep moving forward.

Become creative in those times. Use the three ways of dealing with stress.

Avoid

Divert

Embrace

As boundaries become stronger, you become way more honest with yourself about what you can do, which expresses in a mature version yourself.

You start becoming more responsible with what you do, how you do, and when you do.

Then you are a boss.

That boss knows what they want, and they are deliberate with what they do. They are clear with their time, and they execute. They are precise because they understand who they are and base everything on how they feel and think. It is like they have the key to their success and can unlock it as they please.

So if you are trying to balance the life of a super parent and a high-performing businessperson, if you are focused on putting your head down and making it through the grind, stop, you are missing the boat. There is an easier way.

You must follow the road map I have laid out in this book. You must do the little baby steps that become simple. Once you do that, then you let go. You will forget, and lose yourself in the world of feeling what you are capable of. You will start enjoying how you feel. You will enjoy how much more you are able to accomplish without burning out. You will switch easily from businessperson to parent.

You will see this fast world moving slow.

The pain you used to have will turn into a learning experience. You have learned to look for tension. You have learned to look for sensations. Those subtle sensations dictate what is happening in your world, giving you your own superpower.

There is no need to worry anymore.

As you start to do more work within yourself in a safe way, you will begin to produce, and you will become way more productive.

Your time wasting will be a thing of the past. You now will know what is good for your physical body. You will be mentally clear and focused, taking rapid action. You will be emotionally sound and balanced, being the rock when needed and able to play like a child to let go.

You will be at ease and relaxed because when shit hits the fan, you have your first domino that will set up a chain reaction of events that puts you on top, a place of hyperproductivity.

Chapter 10

You're Not Alone Anymore

So here we are. You have learned the exact step-by-step plan I have used on myself and hundreds of clients. It is the plan I developed after I lost my vision and got it back the second time around. It is the same step-by-step plan I use with my clients to bring back productivity and double their income. The people who have used this plan successfully have ended the drains in their life and started to ground before taking action. This gives them a natural advantage to get ahead in the difficult world.

I have to say, while the book provides real solutions to problems every person faces—physically not feeling good in your skin, so you don't show up as your best self; mentally and emotionally being overwhelmed and feeling like you are stuck in the rat race—I know there are plenty of other solutions out there, and I appreciate you choosing this one.

If you enjoyed this book, I want you to know I will be writing more in the future to help my Live Pain-Free family. I have two groups on paid for the person who want to really change faster with my assistance. and the complimentary live pain free private group on Facebook.

HTTPS://WWW.PATRICKLEROUGE.COM/OFFERS/DohX2d5f

Now you should see that this book, while adding tremendous value, is also designed to help people join a tribe and community. If you received any value from this book at all, I invite you to come on over and join the conversation in the Live Pain-Free family. The reason for this is that we still have a tremendous amount of work to do.

This book works even if you are working with other health care providers on your journey to a better you or you already have a plan. This is jet fuel for whatever you are currently doing, to help you get the results you need, whether it is doubling your income, eliminating the pains that drain your mind and energy, deepening an intimate relationship with your family and your spouse, or even speeding healing after surgery.

In the group, we are going to be covering these things more in depth, all complimentary.

I am doing this to ensure your success. A pain-free life is what you ultimately deserve and getting everything done is part of that. We have to get it into our head that it can be easy.

I am a firm believer in giving away as much value as possible. The right clients who want to work hand-in-hand with me will reach out. Potentially, at this point, you are one of those clients, and I am going to make it so easy for you. I am going to put a link to my calendar for a one-on-one appointment just so we can get to know each other. And, yes, me knowing that you are coming from a link from this book matters.

You already have all the parts and the pieces to begin to get everything you want done. In addition to bringing the knowledge that you've gained from this book to help you grow much faster, I also have three mastermind meetups that I hold virtually. These are sacred places where you can open up to help you clear your mindset, places to get more energy and eliminate physical pain, all using tactical tips and tricks like the ones you learned here, not just strategy.

Potentially, your business is already exceeding expectations. But you might need a mindset shift to help you explode, to get to new heights and break through your own ceilings. You are not alone, my friend. I have been there hundreds of times before, and I am sure I will be there hundreds more times. An easy way to move past that

HTTPS://WWW.PATRICKLEROUGE.COM/OFFERS/DohX2d5f

I will reach out to you to get into this exclusive group. This is a paid group. It meets weekly and gives one-on-one tactical tips to get what you need done with less effort.

If you want to streamline your process, book a call to set up a quick chat.

The first call is completely free because you have read this book.

Chapter 11

Adding more value to your life

In this chapter, I just want to recap and add more value to the main points of the book for you, so you can put the process together easily and start working with it in your life today.

The first recipe is finding the black holes or energy drains in your body and stopping them.

First, you want to do a body scan. The body scan will show you how to find areas of tightness.

Second, ground. Sit with that area in a grounded manner, seeing where you are tight. Feel what is happening and how is it feeling; feel connected to what's happening. Become mindful of what's happening in your feet, moving up toward your hips and upper body, followed by the daily routine.

Third, use a foam roller and your trigger point therapy balls and stretch those areas.

Instead of doing a search-and-destroy as is often taught, finding the knots and rubbing on them vigorously, I invite you to use the techniques listed above, but look for something to change the next time you do a body scan. The trick is not going too hard; look with that curious eye, explore.

If you need more help with foam rolling, trigger point therapy, and stretching, click the link below. The Live Pain-Free family group covers a lot of that.

HTTPS://WWW.PATRICKLEROUGE.COM/OFFERS/DohX2d5f

We also will help you clear up physical pain.

I have a paid program that walks you through an easy challenge. If you want to jump in and begin to balance your mind and body in 7 days this is for you. Giving you the esults you desire with less work as well. You will receive a special offer because you have read this book. Use the code **"Geteverythingdone"** to get the discount.

HTTPS://WWW.PATRICKLEROUGE.COM/OFFERS/XGCTUC8P

The second recipe is to stop mental pain and overwhelm.

Start with the body scan.

With the body scan, see what areas are tight; see where you are always holding tightness. For mental issues and mental clutter, we need to become more tracking oriented. How often is this mental clutter happening? When does it happen more?

I want you to journal when those instances are happening by tracking your triggers.

Who does it often happen around?

What does your body do?

And when does it happen?

Once you do a body scan, you will start seeing all those same areas of tightness. The trick now is to do your next body scan and see if those areas match up.

If you consistently see matches and synchronicities in your chest, your throat, your stomach every time an issue comes, you now have an area to speak in-depth with me about. Reach out inside the Pain-Free group. I explain what the current area in the body is trying to say. I call this your body's *slang* or *dialectic*.

Your daily routine is doing the grounding and doing the body scan and then journaling and watching how it changes as you identify the triggers.

The third recipe for a pain-free life and getting things done is dealing with emotional stress.

Building off the work you have done so far. These new exercises will take you so much deeper. Giving you even more access to your power and clarity

Riding your emotional stress again starts with the body scan.

Do the journal tracking, but now when you find tightness in an area, begin to speak with it as if it were a child. Identify why that emotion is holding on.

Next, do a mindful body scan throughout the day to see when that area is tightening up. The easiest way to notice when you are triggered is when the pace of your breathing changes.

Breathing patterns are one of the easiest ways to identify when you are triggered. You will move from belly breathing to compressed chest breathing. That will be the time to do a body scan and turn off the power to those areas. Your body has been activated to protect itself, so you will need to decrease the power and tightness.

I hope you enjoyed this book.

These three recipes will further your journey through your life, as well as the ability to live and move pain-free.

THE SIMPLE PATH

TO GETTING EVERYTHING DONE

For the Businesswoman Who Needs to Get It All Done

In an age where there is so much demand for us to be "perfect," sometimes it seems everything you do is not noticed or appreciated. If it is noticed, it's when you're down on one knee about to scream in frustration. And the cycle repeats day in and day out. This book shows you the path to making a BIG IMPACT and BIG INCOME, showing you that you can have it all without burnouts, and it has never been easier.

In the Successful Businesswoman's Guide to Getting Everything Done, you will learn:

- ✓ **How to tap into unlimited energy from your body to get even more done**
- ✓ **A step-by-step plan to create a chain reaction that brings out your confidence in the toughest situations**
- ✓ **How to rapidly clear your mind and shift from a highly successful boss to a sweet, loving mom**
- ✓ **How to feel fit and sexy in your skin by doing less and get better results**
- ✓ **How to have an advantage by tapping into your intuition**

It's time to follow a proven path that works, one that adapts to your every need. In today's competitive world, you need to unite and access your natural superpowers, giving you the advantage to get to the top. Too many female business owners struggle to **exist** in two separate worlds—business and home. They barely keep it together, not knowing there is a different, more effective way. Using this simple, natural way, you can **thrive** as a super parent and a highly successful business owner.

Made in the USA
Middletown, DE
13 January 2022

58393970R00062